A CHILDREN'S STORY

Downy Duckling

by Willy Schermelé

This series includes the following titles:

PLUCKY PUFFTAIL
DOWNY DUCKLING
OLLY NOLLY ELEPHANT
TUBBY AND TOOTSY

DOWNY DUCKLING

Downy was a teeny-weeny duckling. His best friend was Cheepy, a little chick who had lost his way. Downy's Mother now looked after Cheepy, and therefore was his foster-mother.

That Downy and Cheepy were such good friends, was mainly because Cheepy *could* not swim and Downy *would*

not swim. Although Downy had feet with webs between his toes, he had a great dislike for the water. Very early every morning he looked wistfully out of the window, when his brothers and sisters were splashing in the pond and standing on their heads. Downy could not even say who was who, because he only saw their tails.

The most wretched thing was that the ducks were always making fun of Downy. More so now Mother had just bought him a sailor-suit to give him pride.

But Downy would not wear it, because the others laughed.

"A sailor-suit, think of it! A sailor who was afraid of water!"

Every morning Downy and Cheepy had to be washed in the tub. Cheepy was a quiet boy when bathed. "I am not so much afraid of water", he chirped, "but more of drowning."

"That's easy to understand", said Mother. "Your feet are different, you will drown in deep water. But Downy is a duckling."

And Mother splashed water over her little son.

Downy made such a noise, that it became a whole family affair. All the ducks were laughing at him and making fun of him.

Only Father and Mother were deeply ashamed and

scolded him. But Mother Duck could not be cross with Downy for long. She was a sweet, kind-hearted duck and she often said to her husband:

"We must not hurry Downy, that will only make him more frightened. One day he will show he is a real duck." Meanwhile, Downy was very, very sad. He longed to play with the other ducks, but not on the water. As always he complained to Cheepy.

"What can the reason be that I hate the water so?", he quacked miserably.

"Maybe you are not a duckling at all", chirped Cheepy.

"Oh, nonsense, I am a duckling," quacked Downy a little hurt.

"Well, you must prove it", said Cheepy, "that is the only way." But Downy thought better. "Let's go blowing bubbles", he suggested.

It was washing-day, so there were plenty of soapsuds.

As the days passed and Downy didn't show any desire for the water, Mother became worried. One day she

decided to go to Dr. Daniel Drake for advice. After lunch she went there with Downy and Cheepy. Downy looked uneasy.

When they entered the Doctor's room, the wise old man quacked to Mother Duck: "Take his shirt off!"

"What does he want with your shirt?", whispered Cheepy.

"Be quiet!", said the Doctor sternly.

Downy had to sit on Mother's knee, and he looked really scared. Then Dr. Drake did some strange things. He listened to Downy's chest, and the poor duckling was ordered to breathe very deeply. This was difficult, because Downy could hardly breathe at all, as he was so frightened.

"Open your mouth!", the Doctor said, "and say A!"

Downy had just learned his A.B.C. and wanted to please the Doctor. "A, B, C, D, E . . . !", he quacked.

"Stop!", roared the Doctor angrily.

Downy tumbled from Mother's lap, scared to death. While he was dressing, the Doctor told Mother not to

worry. There was nothing wrong with Downy, whatsoever. He was the healthiest duckling there could be.

Mother Duck and the chicks felt so happy, that they went home singing.
Downy and Cheepy helped Mother that afternoon in the house.
First they dusted and swept, then they helped in the kitchen. And all the time the little boys were laughing and imitating Dr. Drake. Even Mother had quite a laugh. She too was happy that her son was healthy. She wanted to give an extra treat for supper and promised them pancakes.

Next day Mother said to Downy: "Now that Dr. Drake told us that nothing is wrong, you must prove it by having swimming-lessons."

"Oh Mother", wailed Downy, "let's talk about something more pleasant."

"All right then", quacked Mother, although she did not  agree. "Here is the shopping-bag and there is the list. Go to the grocer. Father is going fishing tomorrow and he likes to take all the ducklings along for a picnic."

Mother gave her boy a soft peck and Downy went away with Cheepy.

The bag was a heavy thing, but they rested now and then. There was always a lot to see in the shop. And the grocer was a kind man who gave the small boys some sweets.

"You are not to carry the shopping-bag home", he said, "I'll bring it along."

It was lovely weather when Father took the small fry to the pond next day. But although both Downy and Cheepy liked a picnic, trouble started after a while.

The ducklings teased Downy and laughed at him.

The frogs also made fun of him, especially a cheeky one, Freddy Hopper.

"Come on now", said Father. "Take off your suit and show us that the Doctor is right and you are really an ordinary duckling. I'll take care that you will not drown."

But Downy looked frightened. "The w...w...water is so w...w...wet", he stammered.

"I'm coming too, boys!", Father laughed and quacked, and started to undress himself.

Downy thought it now better and safer to disappear.

"Who ever heard of a duckling being afraid of water?", Downy quacked unhappily.

"I'm not fond of water either", chirped

Cheepy. "With you it is different", answered Downy. "When you grow up you will get a beautiful red comb, and you can crow "Cock-a-doodle-doo!" There will be plenty of things for you to do."

Cheepy felt very pleased with himself. He touched his

head as if he could already feel the beginning of a comb.

Oh yes, he felt something, and he started to skip.

The two chicks were a good distance from home now and they should have been more careful. But Cheepy didn't think of danger when he hopped away because he felt so happy.

Suddenly ... he found himself in front of the Fox!

Downy who came sauntering along slowly, saw the danger his little friend was in.

Although Cheepy would have been but a mouthful, the

big Fox was hungry. "Swoosh!", went the stick, but the Fox missed.

In the flash of a moment Cheepy turned round and rushed away, straight towards the pond. He jumped from a log into the water.

"Splash!" went a thousands drops of water, and down went Cheepy. But alas, the poor chick could not swim. Things would have been rather black for him, if . . . . . .

Well, you can guess what Downy did, can't you? From behind a tree he saw his little friend take to his heels. And Downy ran too!

The Fox snorted when he saw both the chicken and the duckling had escaped, for he couldn't reach them any more.

At this moment a wonderful thing happened. When Downy headed for the pond to rescue his little pal, he

didn't think if the water were cold or wet. He only thought to save his brave friend. He ran to the bank and plunged into the water. ,,Bubble, bubble, bobble, bobble!" went the water.

Downy swam a long way under the water, till he came near Cheepy. He pulled the little chick to the surface and then quacked: "Climb on to my back!"

Cheepy gasped and spluttered ... "Blob ... blob ... blob!", he said. And with some effort he sat at last on Downy's back. How miserable poor Cheepy looked! He was sticky and dripping. Downy on the contrary looked as downy as ever. He rather enjoyed the water and swam with strong strokes. He was proud and pleased with himself.

You can guess what a wonderful adventure it was for Downy. He had been under the water right to the bottom of the pond.

When he came home, Father was just back from fishing, and the whole family had tea. Poor little Cheepy looked awful. Mother took a big towel and rubbed the little chick till he was all downy and fluffy again.

In the meantime Downy told Father and Mother what had happened. He didn't boast about the rescue, but he told about his dive in the pond. How he had seen all the green plants and the fishes, and how well his webbed feet had worked.

"Well, Mummy and Daddy", he quacked, "I have proved after all that I am a real duckling and I don't think I will be afraid of the water any longer."

Now that Downy had a sudden longing to swim, it was no fun for little Cheepy to sit on the bank and watch. It didn't even please him any more that he felt the tiny beginning of a comb on his head.

But one sunny day something happened that changed Cheepy's life. He was sitting on the grass looking at the spray of diamond drops the ducklings were making in the water.

He felt left-out and lonely. Then suddenly he heard:

"Cluck! Cluck! Cluck!", and he saw a nice, kind and oh, such a familiar face. He guessed at once who it was. It was Mrs. Katy Cackle, his own, dear, lovely Mummy! How happy Mrs. Cackle was to find her own baby-boy! She recognized him from a tiny spot on his wing.

Of course she had tea with Mother Duck, who had been such a good foster-mother. She kissed Mother Duck and thanked her a thousand times, and so did Cheepy.

You will understand that Cheepy would now return with his Mummy. At home he had a big rooster for a father, one who could stretch his neck and crow: "Cock-a-doodle-doo!"

And into the bargain he had two brothers and three sisters. So he would never be lonely.

But although Downy and Cheepy said goodbye, they promised to see each other once in a while.

Downy could put on his sailor-suit at last. He was no longer ashamed of it, because now he was a good swimmer and could splash as well as any duck. He had such a longing for the water, that he made up for lost time. He found it very different swimming in a pond from bathing in a tub.

When Downy parted from Cheepy at last, he pretended to be a big sailor. He took as a boat the tub that had once been used as his bath.

Cheepy waved and just wiped a tear. But he was going to be happy too!

Now there began an entirely new life for Downy. The real life for a duckling. He met all kinds of mysterious things underneath the surface of the pond. The fishes passing by like flashes of silver, the green ferns rocking to and fro. And then the frogs! Oh boy, how Downy teased them now! But of course became good friends with all of them. He knew that it had been very, very silly of him to be afraid of the water.

Downy and Cheepy never forgot each other, oh no! They always remained close friends. Maybe one day you will hear of them again.